CW0A394633

MICHAEL ROSE
TEN DANCES
IN A POPULAR LATIN-AMERICAN STYLE

THE ASSOCIATED BOARD OF
THE ROYAL SCHOOLS OF MUSIC

TEN DANCES

MICHAEL ROSE

1

2
Zortzico

3

Moderato giusto–leggiero (♩ = 116)

4

5
Tango

6
Habanera

Molto andante – flessibile ($\quarternote = 58$)

7
Pasodoble

Allegro marziale ($\unicode{x2669}$ = 126)

8
Cha-Cha

Allegro leggiero ($\quad$ = 66)

9
Bolero

10
Samba

Reproduced and printed by
Halstan & Co. Ltd., Amersham, Bucks., England

EASIER PIANO PIECES

ABRSM PUBLISHING

The Associated Board of
the Royal Schools of Music
(Publishing) Limited

14 Bedford Square
London WC1B 3JG

ISBN 1-85472-699-4

9 781854 726995